Peppa Pig™

The Official Annual

This Peppa Pig book belongs to

....

This book is based on the
TV Series 'Peppa Pig'
'Peppa Pig' is created by
Neville Astley and Mark Baker

Peppa Pig © Astley Baker Davies
Ltd/ Contender Ltd. 2003

www.peppapig.com

Published by Ladybird Books Ltd 2008
A Penguin Company
Penguin Books Ltd, 80 Strand, London, WC2R ORL, UK
Penguin Books Australia Ltd, Camberwell, Victoria, Australia
Penguin Books (NZ), 67 Apollo Drive, Rosedale, North Shore 0632,
New Zealand (a divison of Pearson New Zealand Ltd)

CONTENDER

Contents

The Boat Pond

Peppa, George, Mummy and Daddy Pig are at the duck pond. The ducks are very happy.

"Quack! Quack! Quack!"

Peppa and George have brought their toy boats to race on the pond. George's boat has to be wound up.   "Click, click, whirrr!"

"Your boat doesn't need winding up, Peppa," says Mummy Pig.
"It just needs a little help," says Daddy Pig, blowing Peppa's boat along.

Here is Peppa's friend, Suzy Sheep. "Hello everyone!" she cries. "I've got my speedboat. It has batteries to make it go!"

Woof! Here is Danny Dog, with Grandad Dog. "My Grandad made me this paddle boat. It's steam powered!" gasps Danny Dog.

Rebecca Rabbit arrives with her mummy. "I wish I had a boat," she says. "I've got an idea," says Daddy Pig, picking up his newspaper...

"When I was a little Piggy, I used to fold newspaper to make paper boats!" says Daddy Pig, handing a boat to Rebecca Rabbit.

"Squeak! Thank you Mr Pig," says Rebecca, placing her paper boat on the pond. "Grunt! Grunt!" George wants a paper boat too!

Daddy Pig makes paper boats for everyone! "Let's race!" says Mummy Pig. "Ready, steady, BLOW!" The boats speed across the pond.

"We have a winner!" says Daddy Pig. "That's George's boat!" says Peppa. "George is the winner!" "Hooray!" everybody cheers.

"I like paper boats the best!" cries Peppa. "Me too!" cry all the children. It's time to go home. Everybody has had a great time.

"Bye, bye ducks!" grunts Peppa. The ducks enjoyed the toy boats, but they like having their pond back too.   "Quack! Quack!"

What Comes Next?

What comes next in each series of pictures? Point to the right picture.

1.  ?

2.  ?

3.  ?

4.  ?

10

Lost Toys

George has lost his toys. Help him find them. Then, draw the right toy in the white shapes.

a. b. c.

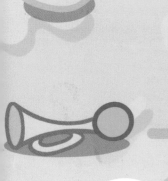

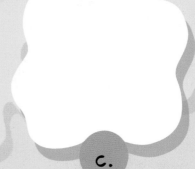

a. b. c.

11

Things to do on a Rainy Day

Ask an adult to help with these activities.

Make Pancakes

Pancake Batter
(makes 6 pancakes)

You will need:
· 120g plain flour
· 1 pinch salt
· 2 eggs
· 210ml milk mixed
with 90ml water

What to do:
Mix the flour and salt in a bowl. Make
a hole in the centre and crack the eggs
into it. Beat the eggs into the flour
with a fork. Stir in the milk and water
mixture until you get a smooth liquid.
Let it settle for 30 minutes before
asking an adult to cook the pancakes
for you!
Serve with syrup or lemon and sugar!

Delicious!

Roll a Dinosaur Game

You will need:
· 2 friends to play with you
· Some paper and a pencil each

What to do:
Take it in turns to roll the dice. The
first person to roll a 6 starts by
drawing the body of a dinosaur. Each
time you roll a number draw a different
part of your
dinosaur using
the key below.

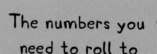

The numbers you
need to roll to
draw each body part are:

6 - body
5 - neck and head
4 - for each leg
(the dinosaur has 4 legs)

3 - for each eye
2 - scales on
its back
1 - scary teeth!

The first person to complete their
picture is the winner.

"Grrrr!"

Things to do on a Sunny Day

Blow bubbles!

To make homemade bubble mixture you will need:

- 2 large cups of water
- 2 tbsp washing-up liquid
- 1 plastic ring

What to do:

Mix the water with the washing-up liquid in a clean bowl. Soak your plastic ring in the mixture and blow carefully. The slower you blow, the bigger the bubble will be!

If you want to make lots of little bubbles, dip your plastic ring into the mixture and run around. You will leave a trail of bubbles behind you!

Hopscotch

You will need:

- One or more friends
- Chalk
- A surface you can draw on
- A pebble

What to do:

Draw a hopscotch grid on the ground with your chalk, with numbers in each square going from 1 to 10. Take it in turns to throw the pebble first to square 1, then hop and jump to the end and back without treading on the lines. Then, throw the pebble onto each of the other squares in order and go to the end and back.

If you fall or touch a square with a pebble you must start from square 1 again! The first one to reach 10 is the winner.

```
        10

      8    9

         7

      5    6

         4

      2    3

         1
```

Breakfast Time

Use your brightest pencils or pens to colour in this picture of Peppa and her family having their breakfast together.

Counting Fun

Carefully count up all the objects in each row.
Then, write the numbers in the white shapes.

Pretend Picnic

Zoe Zebra has a toy picnic set. Use this picture to fill in the circles with the right colours.

Peppa's dress

The grass

The teapot

17

Happy Home

Join the dots to finish the picture of Peppa's house.
Then draw Peppa's friends at the windows.

Window Watch

What can Peppa and George see out of their window? Draw a scene in the space.

Oink! Oink!

Peppa, George, Mummy and Daddy Pig love to laugh! Oink! Oink!

Oink!

Oink!

Oink!

Oink!

Oink!

22

Colour by Numbers

Peppa likes to help Mummy Pig when she is working.
Use the numbers below to colour in the picture.

Peppa's Car Ride

It's a lovely sunny day. Peppa and her family are going for a drive. Peppa and George love their red car.

Clank! Boing! Oh dear. The car does not sound very well. They must take it to Grandad Dog's garage.

Grandad Dog lends them a new blue car. It has lots of different buttons. One of the buttons folds the roof down.

25

Oh dear, it's starting to rain.
Daddy Pig cannot find the button to close
the roof and sprays himself with water!
Peppa and George think this is very funny.

Hee! Hee!

Ha! Ha!

Now Grandad Dog has mended their car. The new car was fun, but Peppa likes their old car the best.

27

Shadow Play

Who can you see in the shadows?
Write in their names.

1.

2.

3.

4.

Answers: 1. Peppa Pig. 2. George. 3. Suzy Sheep. 4. Pedro Pony.

Family Trip

Peppa and her family love to
go for a drive in their car.

Odd One Out

Mummy Pig has asked Peppa and George to sort out their toys before going out to play. Can you point to the odd one out in each row?

Fancy-dress Quiz

Look at the picture of Peppa's fancy- dress party
and answer the questions below.

1. What is Peppa holding in her hand?
2. How many balloons are in the room?
3. What colour is Rebecca Rabbit's carrot costume?
4. What is Danny Dog dressed up as?
5. Who is dressed up as a scary dinosaur?

Peppa Door Hanger

Make your own Peppa door hanger!

What to do:
When you've finished reading this book, cut out these pages and stick them onto thin card. If you don't want to cut up your book, then photocopy these pages. Then, cut along the dotted lines, fold the hanger in half and slot it over your door handle.

Ask an adult to help with cutting out!

George's Birthday

"We're going somewhere very special for George's

birthday treat!" says . "Yippee!" says and

off they all go together.

The family arrives at the museum. "What do you like best

in the whole world ?" asks .

"Dine-Saws!" says George, excitedly.

The birthday treat is a visit to the dinosaur room.

"Grunt," says , jumping up and down.

"Beep. Beep. Rooooaaarrrr!" says a great big dinosaur.

 is very surprised and starts to cry.

"Don't be frightened, it's not a real dinosaur, ,"

explains .

 loves the dinosaur now he knows it's a robot.

"Surprise!" George's friends are here! has made a

birthday cake for .

"It's a dinosaur cake!" says . "Happy birthday,

 ," everyone shouts.

"There's one last surprise," says .

Everybody follows outside. "What's that?"

asks  .

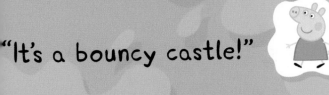 switches on a pump. "It just needs to be filled

with air," he says.

"It's a bouncy castle!" cries.

"No! It's a dinosaur! A bouncy dinosaur!" shouts .

"Hee, hee, hee, grunt! Dine-saw!" says , happily.

Beach Day

Peppa has found something on the beach. Can you guess what it is? Join the dots to see.

Sand Fun

George is building a sandcastle with his bucket.
Help him by drawing it in the space.

Playtime!

Peppa and George are having lots of fun painting pictures!

Questions:

a. How many glasses can you count?

b. How many paintbrushes can you count?

c. How many crayons can you count?

'P' is for Peppa

Use this page to write or draw lots of different things beginning with the letter 'p'.

Mysteries

Peppa and her family are watching their favourite television programme, Detective Potato. "Ooooohhh!" they gasp together.

Mademoiselle Potato needs help. "I cannot find my flower!" "Hmm," thinks Detective Potato. "It is on top of your head!"

"When I grow up, I want to be a famous detective," says Peppa. George wants to be one too. "You'll need these hats," says Daddy Pig.

"We need one of those things, that makes everything look big," says Peppa. "A magnifying glass!" says Mummy Pig, finding one.

"You hold it in front of things and they look bigger," says Mummy Pig. It makes George's eyes look very big. "Ha Ha!" laughs Peppa.

"Now, I'll give you a mystery to solve," says Daddy Pig. "Look hard and try to remember all of the things on the table."

"Okay. You have to go outside. I'll call you when I'm ready." Peppa listens, "It sounds like Daddy is going up and down the stairs."

Daddy Pig calls the detectives back inside. "What is missing from the table?" he asks. "Teddy!" says Peppa. "That's right!" says Daddy Pig.

"But where has Teddy gone?" asks Daddy Pig. Peppa uses her magnifying glass and sees some cake crumbs on the floor.

Peppa and George follow the trail of cake crumbs until they reach their bedroom. "The crumbs have stopped!" says Peppa.

"Is Teddy somewhere in this room?" asks Peppa. "Yes!" replies Daddy Pig. Peppa looks around the room. "Hee hee!" she cries.

"Teddy's in my bed!" Hooray! The mystery is solved. "Being a detective is hard. I want to make mysteries like you, Daddy!" says Peppa.

43

Mystery Quiz

Can you remember what happened in the Mysteries story? Answer the questions and use the pictures to help you.

1. What is Peppa and her family's favourite television programme?

....

2. What did Peppa find on the floor with the magnifying glass?

....

3. Who were Peppa and George trying to find?

....

44

Matching Pairs

Match these things into pairs, by pointing to each one. Which one is the odd one out?

a.

b.

c.

d.

e.

f.

g.

h.

i.

Answers: The pairs are: 'a' and 'h', 'b' and 'g', 'c' and 'd', and 'e' and 'i'. The odd one out is 'f'.

Colouring Game

Play this great game with a friend.

You will need:
· Colouring pencils
· A dice

What to do

Choose a picture to colour each, then take it in turns to roll a dice. Follow the instructions on what to colour when you roll each number. The first person to colour in their whole picture is the winner!

1 = ears
2 = eyes
3 = nose
4 = head
5 = body
6 = ball

1 = crown
2 = eyes
3 = nose
4 = head
5 = body
6 = wings

47

Peppa's Party

Peppa is having the best party ever!

Point to your favourite fancy dress costume.

48

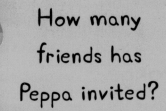

How many friends has Peppa invited?

How many different hats can you spot?

Who is holding a magic wand?

Spot the Difference

It's a sunny autumn day and Peppa and George are playing in the leaves with Mummy and Daddy Pig.

Can you spot the five differences between these two pictures?

Answers: 1. The sun has disappeared. 2. Daddy Pig's hat has changed colour. 3. Peppa has lost her hat. 4. Peppa's boots are red. 5. Daddy Pig has lost his glasses.

Leaf Maze

Mummy Pig is covered in a pile of leaves. Can you help Peppa find her?

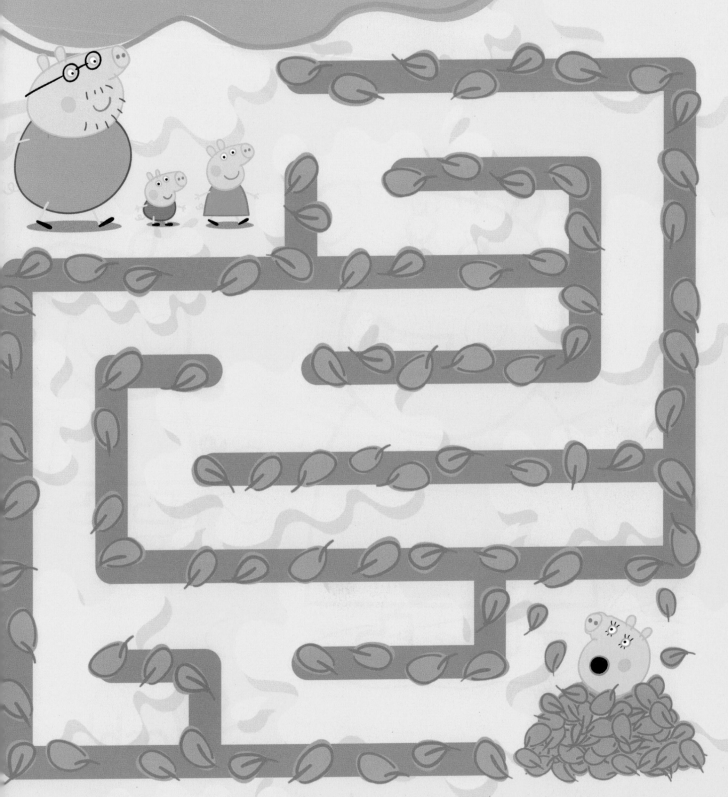

Muddy Puddles

Everyone loves jumping up and down in muddy puddles. Splish, splash, splosh!

53

Noisy Day

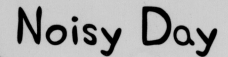

Peppa and George like to watch Mr and Mrs Potato on television.

The Potatoes make them laugh so much that they

"Oink!"   "Oink!"

"Oink!"

Peppa and George love to play in the fluffy, white snow.

When Peppa slips and falls over they both laugh "Oink!"

"Oink!" "Oink!"

Peppa loves to ride on her bicycle.
She sometimes shows off a little.

Peppa lands on her bottom with a thud and shouts

"Oink!"

As Peppa sleeps, the tooth fairy comes to collect her tooth.

When Peppa wakes up, she finds a shiny coin. "Oink!" snorts Peppa happily.

Bedtime

It is almost bedtime. Peppa and George are finishing supper. Daddy and Mummy Pig are yawning, but George and Peppa aren't sleepy.

"Can we play outside for just a tiny bit? Please!" asks Peppa.

"Ho, ho!" laughs Daddy Pig. "OK. But you must come in when it is time for your bath."

Peppa and George have lots of fun playing outside. George loves jumping up and down in muddy puddles.

It's time for Peppa and George's bath.

"Oh. Can't we just play outside a bit longer?" asks Peppa.

"No," replies Daddy Pig. "It's bath time. Aren't you sleepy yet?"

"We're not even a tiny bit sleepy!"

Before bedtime, Peppa and George have their bath. They both like splashing. Hee! Hee!

"That's enough splashing!" cries Daddy Pig. "Let's get you dry and into your pyjamas."

"Can't we just stay in the bath a little bit longer?" asks Peppa.

"No. It's time to clean your teeth," replies Daddy Pig. Peppa and George brush their teeth.

"That's enough brushing. Into your beds!" cries Mummy Pig.

"When you're in bed, Daddy will read you a story." Peppa and George climb into bed.

"Are you sleepy?" asks Daddy Pig.
"No Daddy. We need lots of stories," replies Peppa.

"Daddy Pig will read you one story," says Mummy Pig. "Now which book do you want?"
"The Red Monkey book!" cries Peppa.

"Once upon a time, there was a red monkey," begins Daddy Pig. "And this red monkey had a bath. And cleaned his teeth. He got into his bed. And he soon fell fast asleep. Goodnight red monkey." Snore! Snore! Snore! Peppa and George are asleep. Goodnight!

Mummy and Daddy Pig go downstairs to watch television.
"I've been looking forward to watching this programme," says Daddy Pig, yawning. But just as it starts, Mummy and Daddy Pig both fall asleep. Snore! Snore! Snore! It is bedtime for Peppa and George and it looks as if it is bedtime for Mummy and Daddy too!

Time for Bed

Join the dots to find Peppa and George tucked up in their cosy beds. Goodnight everybody!

Peppa Pig Products
Available at www.peppapig.com

Toys!

Games!

Stickers & Magnets

3 Weekly Magazine

Books

New Framed Pictures

Signed by the creators and exclusive to the animation Art Gallery. Visit w.theanimationartgallery.com

DVDs

Lunch Bags & Umbrellas

ightwear & Clothing for Boys & Girls

Slippers

Clocks & Watches

edroom Accessories

Ready Bed

Pop up Role Play Tent

CD Rom

Products shown above only a small selection of ranges on sale. Full ranges are available online at www.peppapig.com or at all good high street retailers, grocers, stationers, bookstores, toy stores, DVD stockists and catalogues.